The New Scribner Music Library

DR. HOWARD HANSON

EDITOR-IN-CHIEF

VOLUME 2

Keyboard Panorama

Edited by

BLANCHE WINOGRON

CHARLES SCRIBNER'S SONS · NEW YORK

PRINTED IN THE UNITED STATES OF AMERICA
Library of Congress Catalog Card Number 72-1488

SBN 684-13103-X (Volume 2)
SBN 684-13100-5 (Vols. 1-10 with Reference Volume, including Index)

Preface

THE *New Scribner Music Library* is fortunate in having as the editor of the second volume, *Keyboard Panorama*, the distinguished pianist, harpsichordist, and teacher, Blanche Winogron.

Miss Winogron has appeared extensively in concert and on radio and television, throughout the United States and Canada. She is a specialist in the literature of the virginals and her recordings are known in Europe as well as in America. She is equally well known for her History of Keyboard lecture-recitals on this instrument and has appeared in this capacity at the White House.

Her interest, however, is by no means limited to music of the Renaissance and Baroque eras. She has been heard on many occasions in the music of later periods, both with orchestra and with smaller ensembles. She has been associated with the New York Pro Musica and is a founding member of the Consort Players.

Miss Winogron, formerly of The Mannes College of Music in New York and now on the faculty of The New England Conservatory in Boston, is both an inspiring and a meticulous teacher. With her broad background of performance and scholarship she has produced a veritable "panorama" of keyboard music, extending from the fourteenth through the nineteenth centuries, including copious examples of music of the Renaissance, Baroque, Rococo, Classical, and Romantic periods. Both teacher and student will find her selection of compositions from these diverse periods fascinating and stimulating.

HOWARD HANSON

Introduction

VOLUMES 2 and 3 of *The New Scribner Music Library* together comprise a comprehensive view of forms, styles, and idioms in keyboard music, as they have evolved over the centuries. The compositions in these volumes therefore have neither been arranged according to technical difficulty nor in strict chronological order, but rather according to certain structural, stylistic, and expressive aspects, as these have developed historically.

Volume 2, *Keyboard Panorama*, deals chiefly with the simpler forms: two-part dances, variations, short descriptive pieces, and the pre-Classical one-movement sonata, leaving the more involved musical structures to Volume 3.

The volume begins with early instrumental settings of songs and dances, such as the anonymous *Ritornello* which dates back to about 1350, Paumann's *With All My Heart* (one of the earliest love-song settings extant), de la Torre's *Dance,* and the like.

Music of the Renaissance follows. It is represented chiefly through compositions by some of the foremost masters of the English School of Virginalists. (The virginal, the most popular keyboard instrument in 16th century England, is a small harpsichord, i.e., its strings are plucked rather than struck as in the piano.) Compositions such as the anonymous setting of *My Lady Wynkfylds Rownde,* and the pieces by Giles Farnaby and John Bull, etc., show a sophisticated compositional technique and a highly distinctive style, both of which had a profound influence on all European music of that time. To students and music lovers whose familiarity with older music is largely confined to the works of Bach, Handel, Haydn, and Mozart, the music of the Renaissance offers something of a revelation: it shows that Bach is not the beginning but, rather, the glorious culmination of a long and fascinating musical development.

Some of the English Renaissance pieces in Volume 2 show melodic variations on original or popular secular tunes. Parallels of this technique also occurred in church music, in England and on the continent, as shown here in the chorale treatments by Redford, Steenwick, and Buxtehude. Variations on a bass tune or *grownde,* sacred or secular, provided the seed for the later *Passacaille* by J. K. F. Fischer, and the *Chaconnes* of Louis Couperin and Johann Pachelbel.

From the skilled and imaginative use of melodic and figural imitation came the *Inventions, Sinfonias,* and more extended sonata movements of J. S. Bach and his contemporaries. From the early two-part dance forms came the suite and the one-movement sonata of Domenico Scarlatti and Carlos Seixas. Combinations of these two forms evolved into the Classical sonata.

Music has always been used to express the many moods and describe the important events in the life of man. Early examples of such music are the pieces by Attaignant, Frescobaldi, Marpurg, Louis and François Couperin, Daquin, etc., foreshadowing the famous and charming little genre pieces by Schumann, Mendelssohn, Grieg, and by the countless other composers of the Romantic era. Such pieces occupy most of the second half of the present volume. They were selected with a view toward simplicity of form and expression. The more elaborate examples of descriptive (or "salon") music are found in Volume 3, as well as in several of the other volumes of the *Library,* particularly Volume 5.

BLANCHE WINOGRON

Contents by Composers

[6]

For detailed explanations of the ornaments see the *Guide for Good Ornamentation* on page 6 of Volume 3.

Ritornello

from the *Robertsbridge Codex*

Anonymous
(c.1350)

S.M.L.2

With All My Heart

Song from *Fundamentum Organisandi*

CONRAD PAUMANN
(1409-1473)

Dance

FRANCISCO de la TORRE
(c.1500)

Coranto

Anonymous
(16th century)

★ Play the small notes only during the repeat.

The Kynge's Maske

HENRY VIII (?)
(1491-1547)

Dance

HANS NEUSIEDLER
(1508-1563)

★ Like a drum, tambourin, stamping feet, or hand clapping.
Actual addition of any or all of these is most effective.

Eterne Rex Altissime

JOHN REDFORD
(c.1485-1547)

S.M.L.2

My Lady Wynkfylds Rownde

Anonymous
(16th century)

Play on repeat :

S.M.L.2

Tower Hill

GILES FARNABY
(1560-1640)

*On repeat play one octave higher (both hands).

Doctor Bull's My Selfe
A Gigge

JOHN BULL
(c.1562-1628)

★ A good example of the fluctuating scale.

Galiardo

JOHN BULL

21

Tant que Vivray

PIERRE ATTAIGNANT
(d.1553)

S.M.L.2

Blessed Bethlehem

GISBERT STEENWICK
(d. 1679)

Quietly, legato

★ ♩ on repeat only

Prelude

JOHANN KUHNAU
(1660-1722)

Fantasy

GEORG PHILIPP TELEMANN
(1681-1767)

The Little Tight-Rope Dancer

La Voltigeuse

FRIEDRICH WILHELM MARPURG
(1718-1795)

Notebook for Anna Magdalena Bach*
(c.1725)
1. Polonaise in G Minor

BACH FAMILY

*Compiled by and for Bach's second wife and his older children as an «exercise» book.
It is uncertain which of the Bachs wrote these four pieces; Carl Philipp Emanuel was
only eleven at the time.

2. Minuet in G Major

S.M.L.2

3. Minuet in G Minor

4. Musette in D Major

Solfeggietto

CARL PHILIPP EMANUEL BACH
(1714-1788)

Suite on the Chorale
Auf meinen lieben Gott
I Trust in My Dear Lord

DIETRICH BUXTEHUDE
(1637-1707)

ALLEMANDE
Andante serioso

SARABANDE
Slow

36

GIGUE
Swinging

S.M.L.2

Two Little Preludes

I

JOHANN SEBASTIAN BACH
(1685-1750)

38

II
(Prelude for the Lute)

Two-Part Invention No. 1 in C Major

JOHANN SEBASTIAN BACH

simile

Two-Part Invention No. 8 in F Major

JOHANN SEBASTIAN BACH

Recapitulation

poco rit.

Two Minuets
from the First Keyboard Partita

JOHANN SEBASTIAN BACH

I

II

Minuetto I D.C. al Fine

Musette in D Major

from the English Suite in G Minor

JOHANN SEBASTIAN BACH

Andante pastorale

Passacaille en Rondeau

JOHANN KASPAR FERDINAND FISCHER
(c.1665-1746)

Maestoso

47

*Interpolate the Theme (𝄋 to ⊕) between Sections 2 and 3, and 3 and 4,
and conclude with the Theme after Section 4, thus creating a Rondo form.

S.M.L.2

Andantino and Allegro

PADRE MICHEL ANGELO ROSSI
(c.1600 - c.1674)

Andantino

50

Allegro

★ Octave higher suggested for repeat.

★ Octave higher suggested for repeat.

Allemande and Gigue

JOHANN JAKOB FROBERGER
(1616-1667)

ALLEMANDE

Maestoso

53

GIGUE

Inversion

D.C.

S.M.L.2

Sinfonia in D Minor

GEORGE FRIDERIC HANDEL
(1685-1759)

Saraband in F Major

GEORGE FRIDERIC HANDEL

Suite in G Major

Allemande

GEORGE FRIDERIC HANDEL

★ Played throughout:

Air

Gavotte

Canaris
Gigue from the Canary Islands

LOUIS COUPERIN
(1626-1661)

Suggested as more effective } * and **

Chaconne

LOUIS COUPERIN

Chaconne

JOHANN PACHELBEL
(1653-1706)

68

S.M.L.2

Minuet in F Major

WOLFGANG AMADEUS MOZART
(1756-1791)

Minuet in G Major

WOLFGANG AMADEUS MOZART

Allegretto in F Major

WOLFGANG AMADEUS MOZART

Minuet

from the Opera *Don Giovanni*

WOLFGANG AMADEUS MOZART

*On repeat, right hand is effective one octave higher.

S.M.L.2

Bread and Butter Waltz
for One Finger*

WOLFGANG AMADEUS MOZART

*If played only with glissandi

Rondo in D Major

WOLFGANG AMADEUS MOZART

Soldier's March

Soldatenmarsch

No. 2 in "Album for the Young," Op. 68

ROBERT SCHUMANN
(1810-1856)

The Merry Farmer

Fröhlicher Landmann

No. 10 in "Album for the Young", Op. 68

ROBERT SCHUMANN

Melody

No.1 in "Album for the Young," Op. 68

ROBERT SCHUMANN

Bagatelle

Stückchen

No. 5 in "Album for the Young," Op. 68

ROBERT SCHUMANN

Moderato

p tranquillo

81

S.M.L.2

Short Study

No. 14 in "Album for the Young," Op.68

ROBERT SCHUMANN

Saint Nicholas

Knecht Ruprecht

No.12 in "Album for the Young," Op.68

ROBERT SCHUMANN

Sicilienne

No. 11 in "Album for the Young," Op. 68

ROBERT SCHUMANN

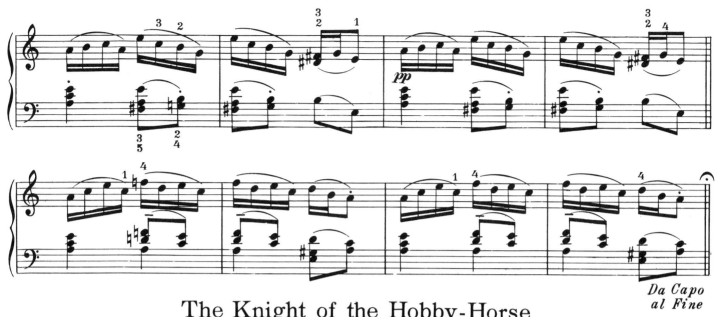

Da Capo
al Fine

The Knight of the Hobby-Horse

Ritter vom Steckenpferd

from "Scenes from Childhood", Op.15

ROBERT SCHUMANN

Allegro con brio

S.M.L.2

The Wild Horseman

Der wilde Reiter

No. 8 in "Album for the Young," Op. 68

ROBERT SCHUMANN

Allegro con brio

The Clock

THEODOR KULLACK
(1818-1882)

from *Children's Album,* Op. 39

Waltz
(No. 8)

PETER ILYICH TCHAIKOVSKY
(1840-1893)

Assai vivo

Reverie
(No.21)

PETER ILYICH TCHAIKOVSKY

Watchman's Song *

Op.12 No.3

EDVARD GRIEG
(1843-1907)

Molto andante e semplice

Intermezzo (Ghosts in the night)

Come prima

ritard.

*Composed after a performance of Shakespeare's Macbeth

Dance of the Elves
Op. 12 No. 4

EDVARD GRIEG

Halling
(Norwegian Dance)
Op.47 No.4

EDVARD GRIEG

Ase's Death

from the *First Peer Gynt Suite*

Op. 46 No. 2

EDVARD GRIEG

S.M.L.2

98

La Frescobalda

GIROLAMO FRESCOBALDI
(1583-1643)

★ Small notes to be played on repeats only.

Variation 2
Gagliarda (Doppio movimento)

Variation 3

Tempo I

Variation 4

Corrente (Allegretto)

Prelude
from Suite No.5

HENRY PURCELL
(c. 1659-1695)

Fanfare

from the Tenth *Ordre* (Suite)

FRANÇOIS COUPERIN
(1668-1733)

* The original has only $\frac{9}{8}$ in the right hand, and just the signs to indicate where ornaments were to be played. None were realized. The present editor has worked them out to fit the $\frac{3}{4}$ left-hand notation.

Les Baricades Mystérieuses

Rondeau from the Sixth *Ordre* (Suite)

FRANÇOIS COUPERIN

110

COUPLET 3

S.M.L.2

Le Coucoû

The Cuckoo

LOUIS-CLAUDE DAQUIN
(1694-1772)

★ The first section is always repeated before the next couplet is played.

COUPLET 2

Gigue in G Minor

JEAN-BAPTISTE LOEILLET
(1680-1730)

Le Tambourin
and
Musette en Rondeau

JEAN-PHILIPPE RAMEAU
(1683-1764)

Le Tambourin *

Allegro

* The Tambourin and Musette are effectively paired like a
Minuet and Trio: Tambourin-Musette-Tambourin (to the end without repeats).

120

Musette en Rondeau(*)
Theme (A) *Tendrement (Tenderly)*

Theme (B)

Fine

Last time repeat
Le Tambourin

Repeat (A)

S.M.L.2 * Pattern of repeats : A-B-A-C-A-B'-A.

Gavotte
from the Opera *Iphigénie*

CHRISTOPH WILLIBALD von GLUCK
(1714-1787)

Fine

dolce

D.C. al Fine

Andante

from the Opera *Orfeo*

CHRISTOPH WILLIBALD von GLUCK

Gavotte

FRANÇOIS-JOSEPH GOSSEC
(1734-1829)

Allemande
"Introduction to Scarlatti"
from the Suite in G Minor

THOMAS ROSEINGRAVE
(1690-1766)

128

Sonata "Pastorale"
L. 413

DOMENICO SCARLATTI
(1685-1757)

Sonata "Tempo di Ballo"

L. 463

DOMENICO SCARLATTI

Sonata

L. 82

DOMENICO SCARLATTI

Sonata
L.238

DOMENICO SCARLATTI

Sonata

CARLOS SEIXAS
(1704-1742)

Andante

CARLOS SEIXAS

★ on repeat only.

Gipsy Rondo

from Trio No.1

JOSEPH HAYDN
(1732-1809)

143

144

S.M.L.2

Ballet Music
from "Rosamunde"

FRANZ SCHUBERT
(1797-1828)

Entr'acte No.5

from "Rosamunde"

FRANZ SCHUBERT

Andantino

Fine

Minore

D.C. al Fine

Moment Musical
Op. 94 No. 3

FRANZ SCHUBERT

Serenade

Ständchen

FRANZ SCHUBERT

Seven Waltzes

from Op.9a

FRANZ SCHUBERT

★ Parenthetical numbers refer to the complete set of Opus 9a.

Für Elise

Album Leaf

LUDWIG van BEETHOVEN
(1770-1827)

Minuet
from Sonata Op. 49 No. 2

LUDWIG van BEETHOVEN

Minuet in G Major

LUDWIG van BEETHOVEN

D.C. al Fine

Bagatelle
Op.119 No.9

LUDWIG van BEETHOVEN

Vivace moderato

Bagatelle

Op. 33 No. 3

LUDWIG van BEETHOVEN

Bagatelle

Op. 119 No. 1

LUDWIG van BEETHOVEN

174

Turkish March
Turkish March

from *The Ruins of Athens*

LUDWIG van BEETHOVEN

S.M.L.2

176

S.M.L.2

Ecossaises

(Scottish Dances)

LUDWIG van BEETHOVEN

Leggiero e animato

Invitation to the Dance

(Rondeau Brillant)

Op. 65

CARL MARIA von WEBER
(1786-1826)

192

S.M.L.2

Five "Songs Without Words"

1. Spring Song

Op. 62 No. 6

FELIX MENDELSSOHN
(1809-1847)

Allegretto grazioso

2. Confidence

Op.19 No.4

3. Venetian Gondoliers' Song

Venetianisches Gondellied

Op. 19 No. 6

Andante sostenuto

4. Consolation

Op. 30 No. 3

Adagio non troppo

5. Spinning Song

Op. 67 No. 4

Presto

p leggiero

206

Mazurka
Op. 68 No. 3

FREDERIC CHOPIN
(1810-1849)

Mazurka
Op. 68 No. 2

FREDERIC CHOPIN

Poco più mosso

legatissimo

poco a poco rit.

Dal Segno
al Fine

S.M.L.2

Mazurka
Op. 7 No. 1

FREDERIC CHOPIN

Five Preludes from Op. 28
No. 4 in E Minor

FREDERIC CHOPIN

No. 7 in A Major

No. 20 in C Minor

No. 23 in F Major

No. 6 in B Minor

Prayer

CARL REINECKE
(1824-1910)

Tarantella
Op. 85

STEPHEN HELLER
(1813-1888)

224

S.M.L.2

Élégie

JULES MASSENET
(1842-1912)

Slowly, with feeling

Lullaby

from the *Nour and Anitra* Suite
Op.13

ALEXANDER ILYINSKY
(1859-1920)

To a Wild Rose

Op.51 No.1

from "Woodland Sketches"

EDWARD MacDOWELL
(1861-1908)

With simple tenderness (♩ =88)

Song

Op. 55 No. 5

from *Sea Pieces*

EDWARD MacDOWELL

Fairy Tale
Op. 26 No. 3

NICOLAI MEDTNER
(1880-1951)

The Flatt'rer

La Lisonjera

CÉCILE CHAMINADE
(1857-1944)

Moderato molto capriccioso

Scarf Dance

CÉCILE CHAMINADE

Menuet à l'antique

IGNACE PADEREWSKI
(1860-1941)

248

S.M.L.2

Fairy Tale

SERGEI PROKOFIEV
(1891-1953)

Danse Fantastique

Op.1 No.1

DMITRI SHOSTAKOVICH
(b.1906)

Prelude

Op.34 No.19

DMITRI SHOSTAKOVICH

Improvisation on a Hungarian Peasant Song

Op. 20 No.1

BÉLA BARTÓK
(1881-1945)

(Full-size notes: down-stems = L.H.;
up-stems = R.H.)

1920